Matt RULEZ!!! —Stephen Notley

Bob the Angry Flower

Coffee With Sinistar

Stephen Notley

• L e f t o v e r   B o o k s •

Foreword by
Dan Harmon

Like Stephen Notley himself, Bob the Angry Flower is smart, funny, accessible and warm. Like Notley himself, Bob will touch an unknown part of you. He'll try to find a way inside you. If you allow Bob that access, like Notley, he will impregnate you and then— guess what? He'll deny it.

In fact, the only difference between that myopic, Canadian rapist and his clownish, fictional plant is that the latter cannot be sued for paternity, whereas the courts have forced Notley to publish my foreword as warning.

Stay frosty, marine: Bob, like Notley, has outwardly likeable characteristics. He'll make you titter at his absurdist hairpin punchlines. You'll begin to admire his macho swipes at society's pillars ("Where is your veil, whore?"). Massaged by his wry, intellectual tendrils, you may even writhe in your seat, cooing, "I remember that name from economics class." This book contains enchanted mirrors, suicide, ogres, lasers, Hamlet, zombies and robots. I know those are things you like. Bob knows that, too— just as Stephen knew what I liked. But that's the scam. You're going to be tittering and cooing and Bob's going to catch you off guard and he's going to let you "have it," prison style. Notley style. I mean over the sink, right up the flim-flam.

Learn from my pain. Think of the neglected, bastard face of "our" son, Stephen junior. When *Coffee with Sinistar* starts to open, see that your legs stay closed.

Dan Harmon is a screenwriter in Los Angeles.

Tiny tiny tiny contents page

BOB
THE ANGRY FLOWER

INCA
DINKA DOO

www.compusmart.ab.ca/snotley/bob.htm

YOU COME FAR AND LEARN MUCH. ONLY ONE STEP LEFT—THE BLOOD OF THE MOUNTAIN. ARE YOU READY TO DRINK?

YES.

THEN DRINK.

sip!

WHOA, HEY, I FEEL A LITTLE...

A LITTLE WOOZY...

Hey did you hear that

SOUND?

I THOUGHT YOU WEREN'T SUPPOSED TO FEED THAT CRUD TO THE TOURISTS ANY MORE...

AH, C'MON, IT'S HILARIOUS! HE'S TOTALLY WASTED!

plplpl...

5

To the SUN

And that was it for *SEE Magazine*. After what seemed like and was months of wrangling, Bob jumped ship and went over to the *Edmonton Sun*, the smaller of the two Edmonton daily newspapers. Bob would run every Sunday on page 2 of the Express section, and man, did I ever not appreciate that consistency at the time.

Going from a relatively free-wheeling weekly environment to the constraints of a daily, "family" newspaper required some big changes, the biggest of which was Bob couldn't swear any more. Luckily, it didn't turn out to be that important; if you've got a big enough vocabulary you can come up with something almost as good as swearing if you push yourself, and if you fail, there's always the dictionary. I hadn't been swearing that much in the strip in the previous few weeks anyway, so I barely noticed when it was no longer allowed. Of course, the accusations of selling out and mellowing out followed soon after, but they were easy to ignore.

The *Sun* was a great environment, though again I didn't realize it at the time. The pressure of running in a daily newpspaper forced me to clean up and fly right, and the cartoon took an almost immediate twist for the better. I cleaned up the art and started not doing the really bad ideas. Around Christmastime at the *Sun* represents some of my favorite Bob cartoons, including ones like "Seven Minutes in Tibet," "Thus Spak Zarathustra," and "The Seduction."

BOB THE ANGRY FLOWER

I FOUGHT TH' LAW

DON'T WALK

DON'T WALK

HOLD IT!

DON'T WALK

scoot scoot scoot scoot scoot

YOU JUST BOUGHT YOURSELF A $50 JAYWALKING TICKET, MY FRIEND!

OH, DID I *REALLY*...

WELL, MR. P'LICEMAN, FOR YOUR INFORMATION, MY **FREEDOM** MEANS MORE TO ME THAN ANY TICKET **EVER** COULD!

NOT TO MENTION THAT I AM SO DAMN *RICH* YOU COULD WRITE A *HUNDRED* OF THOSE TICKETS AND I COULDN'T CARE LESS!

WOO! HEY! I'M REALLY JAYWALKING NOW! LOOK AT ME GO! BETTER GIVE ME ANOTHER TICKET, MISTER **PEE-EYE-GEE**!!!

SO...WHEN DO WE LET HIM OUT?

WE DON'T.

8

BOB
THE
ANGRY
FLOWER

FABRICATED

HEY— IT'S DENIM MAN!

WHAT?

HE WEARS DENIM JEANS, A DENIM SHIRT, *AND* A DENIM JACKET, SO EVERYBODY AROUND TOWN JUST CALLS HIM *DENIM MAN!*

HMPH!

DENIM MAN, EH? WE'LL SOON SEE ABOUT *THAT!*

SIR, IN RESPECT FOR YOUR MASTERY OF DENIM, PLEASE ALLOW ME TO PRESENT TO YOU THIS BERET AS A GIFT.

!

SORRY, BUDDY, NO CAN DO. I ONLY WEAR DENIM.

AH, BUT THIS *IS* DENIM! SOFT, BLACK, *NEW* DENIM!

WHAT ARE YOU TALKING ABOUT? THAT BERET'S MADE OF BLACK *FELT!*

SHHHH!

WELL, IT DOES LOOK PRETTY SHARP...

WICKED SHARP!

AND SO OFF HE WENT WITH HIS BERET, AND ALTHOUGH HE WORE DENIM JEANS, A DENIM SHIRT, AND A DENIM JACKET, HE WAS NO LONGER *DENIM MAN*. HE WAS MERELY... *A DORK.*

HEH HEH HEH

JEEZ...

9

BOB THE ANGRY FLOWER

A FRIENDLY CHAT

B'ob THE ANGRY FLOWER

A CRISIS of FAITH

YES! THAT MARY AND BABY JESUS NIGHT-LIGHT WILL PROTECT ME FROM NOCTURNAL HARM!

AND SO IT DOES!

HURT

HOWEVER...

FTZ! BZT! SRATCH!

NO, MARY AND BABY JESUS NIGHT-LIGHT! PLEASE DON'T BURN MY HOUSE DOWN!

FW OOF!

ALAS...

why?

WHY?

WHY?

BECAUSE:

IT WAS CHEAPLY MADE IN TAIWAN WHERE THEY HAVE NO LABOR OR SAFETY STANDARDS AND DON'T BELIEVE IN GOD!

AND YET SOMEHOW IT STILL SEEMS UNFAIR...

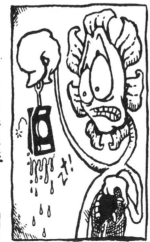

BOB THE ANGRY FLOWER

THE NEW 'DO

JUST A QUICK TRIM — GOT A BIG DATE TONIGHT!

YOU GOT IT!

snip! snip! snip!

MUH-MUH... MY HAIR'S A CONE!

WHOA — YOU'RE RIGHT! THAT HAIRCUT IS TERRIBLE!

WE'VE GOT TO GET YOU CHECKED OUT IMMEDIATELY! COME ON!

HMM.

MMMM...

WELL?

YES — IT'S A CONE. A PERFECT CONE.

GENTLEMEN — CONGRATULATIONS. WE'VE DONE IT.

POP!

YEAH, LIKE I'M GOING TO BE SEEN IN PUBLIC WITH THAT HAIR...

BOB THE ANGRY FLOWER

SUCH A CUTIE!

OHMIGOD! *COREY'S* ON THE COVER OF THIS MONTH'S *TIGER BEAT!*

YOU'RE TOO FAT!

LISTEN TO *THIS!* "I'M HAVING A GREAT TIME MAKING MOVIES, BUT I'M STILL LOOKING FOR THAT SPECIAL SOMEONE."

THAT COULD BE *ME!* OHMIGOD WE COULD GET *MARRIED!*

AND WE COULD LIVE IN A BIG HOUSE IN *CALIFORNIA!*

A-HA!!! *THERE* YOU ARE!

ZZ-ZZ-ZZ!

QUIT YER WRIGGLIN' YOU LITTLE *MONSTER!*

GLUH!

splech!

sploch!

THERE... THAT'S BETTER...

GOD, I LOVE HIM SO MUCH I COULD JUST *DIE!*

THANX JILL!

BOB
THE
ANGRY
FLOWER

KEEP
THE
CHANGE

HEY-THAT'S A SMOOTH SHAVE! I THINK I'LL BUY THE COMPANY!

HEY, FORSBERG! HOW MUCH FOR YOUR COMPANY!

SHAVECORP

THIS MORNING'S STOCK PRICES VALUED A CONTROLLING INTEREST AT $63 MILLION.

WELLLL... I THINK I MIGHT JUST HAVE THAT ON ME...

HMPH.

GASP!

63000000

ONE OF ONLY FOUR IN THE WORLD!

ELMER JENKINS HAS ONE. HIS FRIENDS KEEP ASKING HIM FOR MONEY, SO HE'S HIDING IN THE CLOSET UNTIL THEY GO AWAY.

HEY, MAN-YOU IN THERE OR WHAT?

CAN'T MOVE. CAN'T BREATHE. TOTAL SILENCE.

CELIA MCKEE USED HERS TO BUY 1.26 BILLION LICORICE JAW-BREAKERS FOR HER CAT, JASPER.

meow?

THE OTHER ONE'S FAKE.

THIS IS A JOKE, RIGHT?

OKAY, FROM NOW ON ALL OUR RAZORS WILL HAVE BIG SPIKES AND LASER CANNONS AND BE MADE OF PURE PLUTONIUM!

BUT SIR!

HEY! WHO OWNS THIS COMPANY?

YOU DO, SIR...

15

BOB THE ANGRY FLOWER

THE PAST— AND BEYOND!

HMMM... ROLLER SKATES OR ROLLER BLADES...?

EXCUSE ME.

HEY! YOU'RE ARTHUR MEIGHAN, CANADA'S CONSERVATIVE NINTH PRIME MINISTER!

I AM. I NEED YOU TO GUIDE ME THROUGH YOUR SO-CALLED "1990s."

AND SO BEGINS A BREATHLESS FANTASIA OF MODERNITY!

OH NO!

THAT INDUSTRIAL BEAM KNOCKED YOUR PHOTO-COPIED HEAD RIGHT OFF! HOW DO YOU FEEL?

STRANGELY CALM, ACTUALLY...

POOR STATESMAN OF THE PAST... THE PRESENT WASN'T KIND TO YOU...

BUT WHAT OF THE FUTURE?

EEoooE EoooE EoooE EoooE

THE ALARM! WHAT DOES THE WRIST-SENATE ADVISE?

THEY UNANIMOUSLY VOTE TO KICK SOME FONX!

16

B°B The AnGry fLOwEr

WHEN YER RIGHT, YER RIGHT

www.compusmart.ab.ca/
snotley/ bob.htm

SO, YEAH, THIS WAS AT SOME CANDLE STORE OUT ON THE WEST END SOMEWHERE...

PARDON ME — I COULDN'T HELP BUT OVERHEAR. THAT STORE IS CALLED **WAX N' WAYNE'S**, AT 8307 153rd STREET...

YOU CAN TAKE A NUMBER 53 BUS STRAIGHT THERE, OR JUST DRIVE DOWN BELL ROAD AND TURN LEFT AT 150th!

HELLO — MY NAME IS **MR. CORRECT**, AND IF YOU'D CARE TO VERIFY MY INFORMATION, I'M CONFIDENT YOU'LL FIND THAT IT'S ALL **CORRECT.**

UH-HUH. YEP. SEEMS TO CHECK OUT.

SEEMS YOU'RE AS GOOD AS YOUR WORD, MR. CORRECT. WE HAVE NO CHOICE BUT TO MAKE YOU OUR KING.

...AND IN YOUR NAME, MY LIEGE, WE WILL BRUSH AWAY THIS PUNY DEMO-CRACY AND INSTALL YOU AS *PHILOSOPHER-TYRANT!*

I CAN ALREADY HEAR THE screaming.

WELL, THERE HE GOES, AND HE PROBABLY THINKS YOU'RE DANGEROUSLY INSANE...

OH IN THAT I'D SAY HE'S QUITE **CORRECT.**

17

BOB the ANGRY flower

COPY WRONG

Bill the CRANKY FLOWER only 59¢ with large meal

GUH...

WHOEVER DID THIS WILL BE MADE TO SUFFER

Bob's search soon leads him to Hong Kong!

THERE YOU ARE! YOU'LL PAY FOR RIPPING ME OFF, OLD MAN! - YOU'LL PAY!

PLEASE FORGIVE ME, HONORED SIR. I DID NOT KNOW, I SWEAR. I AM JUST A POOR OLD MAN, YES...

I JUST TRY TO FEED MY FAMILY. I CARVE THE TOYS OUT OF OLD PLASTIC FROM THE DUMP FOR A FEW PENNIES EACH.

A FEW PENNIES...

HEY, MAN... IT'S OKAY...

THAT'S IT, MISTER AUNG - HE'S GIVEN CONSENT.

GOOD. GET THE PRESS-MOLDS ROLLING - WE NEED ANOTHER BILLION TOYS BY TUESDAY...

OLD CHINESE MAN-A-TRON 2000

BOB THE ANGRY FLOWER

BAD CALL

OH! OH! LOOK AT THAT CAR-PHONE-USING VISIGOTH! TAKE THE WHEEL, STUMPY— I'M GONNA NAIL 'IM!

GONNA USE THE OLD SWARM-O-BEES?

HMM... OUT OF BEES...

WHAT ELSE IS THERE...?

BEEP BEEP

OOPS... MY CELLULAR..

OH - DR. BICKFORD! YEAH! HEY- CAN I GET YOU TO HANG ON FOR JUST TWO SECONDS? THANKS!

PIG OUT, YOU LOSER!

WHAM!

Oink

SKREEEE CRA! SH AIE-EE!

oink?

AND NOW I'M WONDERING IF THAT WAS THE BEST THING TO DO, ESPECIALLY SINCE I REALLY NEEDED TO TAKE THAT CALL...

MAYBE I SHOULD CALL AN AMBULANCE...

BEEP BEEP BEEP

BEEP BEEP BEEP

Bob the ANGRY Flower

THE OBLIGATORY DAY-IN-THE-LIFE STRIP

BOB THE ANGRY FLOWER WENT OUT YESTERDAY.

HE BOUGHT SOME MILK...

...BRUSHED OFF HIS LONG-LOST BROTHER WHO WAS BEGGING FOR CHANGE...

...TALKED ABOUT CARROTS WHEN EVERYBODY ELSE WAS TALKING ABOUT MONEY...

$ · $! · !· $%¥ · ¢·

...FACED THE FEARSOME ZORG-BOTS OF INTERSTELLAR FRANCE...

HA! · ZUT ALORS!

...SHARED A MOMENT OF QUIET FAITH WITH CLOSE FRIENDS...

...AND GAVE UP HIS LIFE DEFENDING TO THE DEATH SOMEONE ELSE'S RIGHT TO HOLD DESPICABLE OPINIONS.

LIBERTY

...OR NO, WAIT... HE SPENT MOST OF THE DAY AT HOME.

20

BOB THE ANGRY FLOWER

I SUCK I SUCK WHY CAN'T I DO THIS KILL ME NOW PLEASE I CAN'T TAKE THIS ANYMORE I JUST CAN'T

NOR SHOULD YOU HAVE TO, MR. FLOWER!

OBSERVE! THIS PRODUCT PLUGS INTO YOUR CARTOONA OBLONGATA, SCANS YOUR BRAIN, AND EASILY AND EFFORTLESSLY EXTRACTS A COMPLETE CARTOON!

CHUK

DRRR

HMMM... NOT BAD...

NOT BAD? IT'S A PANIC! YOU'RE VERY TALENTED!

BOB, NO!

HIS OFFER IS A FOOL'S BARGAIN!

NOTHING OF VALUE COMES WITHOUT STRUGGLE! TO SEEK OTHERWISE IS TO DENY THE WORTH OF THE VERY THING YOU CREATE!

DON'T YOU SEE HE'S TRYING TO GET YOU TO GIVE UP YOUR SOUL?

WHAT'S HE JABBERING ABOUT?

GOD, I HAVE NO IDEA...

I ASSUME CASH WILL BE ACCEPTABLE?

21

Bob THE ANGRY FLOWER

M. I. A.

...OFFICIALS REPORT A MASSIVE LEAK OF *FREAK-OUT* GAS, AND ARE WARNING PEOPLE TO BE ON THE LOOKOUT FOR ANY SIGNS OF...WELL, FREAKING OUT, REALLY...

GENTLEMEN, WE ARE IN A CRISIS SITUATION.

SOON THE STREETS WILL BE CRAWLING WITH CANNIBAL LUNATICS SEEKING TO DINE ON A RICH FEAST OF FLOWER, TREE STUMP, AND WHATEVER THE HELL IT IS YOU ARE, FREDDIE...

ARMED RESISTANCE IS OUR ONLY HOPE.

SENTRY DUTY. FOUR A.M.

GOSH- I SURE HOPE THIS ALL BLOWS OVER!

YER A FOOL, KID...

I'VE SEEN TOO MANY GOOD MEN DIE FOR NO REASON, AND NOTHIN' TELLS ME WE'RE ANY DIFF'RENT...

NONE OF US IS GONNA MAKE IT OUT ALIVE

...NONE OF US...

...hffffff...

THERE NEVER REALLY WAS A GAS LEAK, WAS THERE...

...NONE OF US...

23

REWOLF YRGNA EHT

BOB

WHEN **SMARTIAC** COMMANDS!

SMARTIAC, YOU *FIEND!* YOU AND YOUR PERNICIOUS *BRAIN BEAM* HAVE CURSED THESE INNOCENT BYSTANDERS WITH *VASTLY INCREASED INTELLIGENCE!*

IT'S ABSURD TO BLAME YOU FOR MY WORTHLESS LIFE!

A JUST GOD COULD NEVER ALLOW HELL TO EXIST!

YOU'RE ABUSIVE AND I'M LEAVING YOU.

AR HAR HAR HAR

LAUGH WHILE YOU CAN, SMARTIAC, BECAUSE YOUR *REIGN OF BRAIN* IS ABOUT TO END IN *PAIN!*

...THOUGH I'M NOT ALL THAT SUPER CLEAR ON HOW I'M GOING TO PULL THIS OFF...

WELL THEN, FLOWER...

...ALLOW ME TO CLEAR UP SOME OF YOUR TROUBLING *DOUBTS!!!*

HA HA HA HA HA HA HA

THOTZ!

R!

GGGO

AH YES.

OF COURSE.

THUS THE HYPER-INTELLIGENT FLOWER SWIFTLY DEFEATS SMARTIAC WITH A PLAN TOO INGENIOUS TO DEPICT, AGAIN MAKING THE WORLD SAFE FOR IGNORANCE AND THE STATUS QUO, THANK GOD.

YOU'RE SO STUPID!

I'M SORRY, HONEY...

LOOK UNTO SODOM

REPENT OR BURN!

BOB THE ANGRY FLOWER

NOBODY WANTS TO BE LECTURED BY AN INVISIBLE COW

www.compusmart.ab.ca/snotley/bob.htm

AND WOULD YOU LIKE A DRINK WITH THAT?

DID I ASK FOR ONE, YOU SALES-PITCH LACKEY?

DEEP EEP

BUT THE SPICY FOOD WORKS ITS MAGIC...

MAN, I COULD REALLY USE A DRINK...

DIDN'T I SAY YOU'D BE THIRSTY?

DROP DEAD, INVISIBLE COW.

SURE—INSULT ME! IT'S EASY WHEN YOU'RE THE ONLY ONE WHO CAN SEE OR HEAR ME...

BUT I WAS RIGHT, WASN'T I? I'M ALWAYS RIGHT!

NOW IF YOU WANT A DRINK YOU'RE GOING TO HAVE TO MARCH RIGHT OVER THERE AND APOLOGIZE TO THAT NICE CASHIER!

OH YEAH? ACK!

GRAB!

NO, OFFICER—I CAN'T EXPLAIN IT, BUT I'M PRETTY SURE THAT WHATEVER IT IS, IT SHOULDN'T BE HAPPENING...

MOOOO MOOOO MOOO

MOOOO

HA HA HA HAHA!

SPL ORT!

9-27

25

BOB THE ANGRY FLOWER

MUST SEE

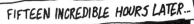

28

BOB the ANGRY FLOWER

SOME WORDS OF CONSOLATION

OKAY, SURE...

SURE - IT WAS BAD LUCK GETTING YOUR HANDS CUT OFF IN THAT TYPING ACCIDENT. THAT'S A BAD ROLL OF THE DICE FOR ANYBODY.

AND YEAH - THE SURGEON WAS SO DRUNK HE ATTACHED YOUR HANDS TO YOUR FOREHEAD. THAT'S A TOUGH ONE. NOBODY'S QUESTIONING THAT. *NOBODY.*

BUT AT LEAST - *AT LEAST* - THEY WERE ABLE TO ATTACH A BIG FROSTY MUG OF BEER TO EACH STUMP, RIGHT? THAT'S NOT TOO BAD!

RIGHT?

SO, SEEING AS HOW YOU LOOK LIKE YOU'VE GOT SOME EXTRA BEER THERE —

GET LOST!

....JERK...

slup

29

BOB THE ANGRY FLOWER

RHETORICAL FLAIR

www.compusmart.ab.ca/snotley/bob.htm

OF COURSE, HISTORICALLY THE RIGHT HAS ALWAYS ADVOCATED FISCAL SANITY AND INCREASED ACCOUNTABILITY TO TAXPAYERS...

OH BROTHER...

LATER... ALL RIGHT—IT'S TIME TO BEAT THIS GUY AT HIS OWN GAME! GET ME MY ECONOMICS TEXTBOOKS!

STUDY EVERYTHING!

SUPPLY

EVERY FACT!

DEMAND

EVERY ARGUMENT!

LEARN IT ALL!

FINALLY... SO? THINK YOU'RE READY FOR HIM?

YOU'D BETTER BELIEVE IT!

...CERTAINLY, SOROS IS A MULTI-BILLIONAIRE, BUT HIS POLITICAL INSIGHTS ARE HOPELESSLY NAIVE...

I DON'T AGREE. ALLOW ME TO REBUT.

HA!

CHUK!

THAT'S RIGHT! I CUT MY HAND OFF!!! WHAT DO YOU SAY TO **THAT**, YOU BUBBLE-TALKING **HYPOCRITE**?!? HUH, RICH BOY? WHAT'ZA MATTER? CAN'T TAKE A LITTLE BLOOD? GET BACK HERE, YOU INTELLECTUAL **COWARD**!

ZOOM!

I'D SAY I WON THAT ONE PRETTY **HAND**ILY, EH?

SURE.

A BRIEF COMMENT ON THE VALUE OF POISE

SPLÖSH!

HOLY-!

NOW THAT'S SOME POISE!

YOU SAID IT!

BOB? COULD I SEE YOU IN MY OFFICE FOR A MOMENT?

WE NEED A MAN WITH POISE TO HEAD UP OUR JAPANESE OFFICE. THINK YOU CAN HANDLE IT?

ABSOLUTELY!

子理！所形！*

<HE SPEAKS GIBBERISH!>

<BUT SEE THE CUP!>

<OBSERVE HIS MIGHTY POISE!>

* HELLO, I AM A DOG.

WE NEED YOU TO AID US IN OUR QUARREL AGAINST THE TERRIBLE MONSTER-GOD!

<HELLO, I AM A DOG!>

SOON...

WHOA!

HEY!

SETTLE DOWN!

SKREEEEUNK

...AH YES... A DIFFICULT BUT FASCINATING PEOPLE, THE JAPANESE...

SIP!

31

BOB THE ANGRY FLOWER

HOW GHOST STORIES GET STARTED

www.compusmart.ab.ca/snotley/bob.htm

dog + cat = cag + dot

...SO IF CAT...HANG ON, THAT'S NOT WESTGATE...

ALL RIGHT—WHERE THE **HELL** IS THIS STUPID BUS GOING?!?

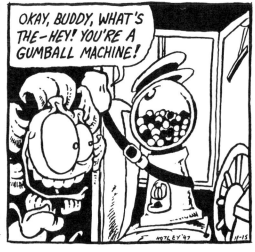

OKAY, BUDDY, WHAT'S THE—HEY! YOU'RE A GUMBALL MACHINE!

MOTLEY '97   11-15

BUT SOON... GIMME **MY GUMBALL** YOU QUARTER-STEALING LITTLE—

ARKK

SMASH!

AND SO BOB FOUND HIMSELF BEHIND THE WHEEL, EVEN THOUGH HE SWORE HE'D NEVER DRIVE A TRANSIT VEHICLE AGAIN. YEARS LATER, SOME STILL SPOKE OF A DIM PHANTOM BUS ROLLING THROUGH THE NIGHT, LEAVING ONLY A MUTTERED CURSE AND — OCCASIONALLY — A FAINT WHIFF OF WATERMELON-FLAVORED BUBBLE GUM.

BOB THE ANGRY FLOWER

PLAYIN' DURTY

LOOK! MY SUPER-VACUUM CLEANER CAN SUCK MONEY RIGHT OUT OF YOUR PANTS!

HAW! I BET ALL THE POL'TICIANS'D LOVE THAT—THEN THEY COULD GET _ALL_ OUR MONEY!

SHLORK!

DUMB CLETUS IS _RIGHT!_ OUR THIEVING GOVERNMENT WOULD REWARD ME WELL FOR MY INVENTION!

$3

$ $

ALAS...

...WELL, MR. FLOWER, I DON'T SEE WHAT USE WE COULD HAVE FOR YOUR DEVICE, ESPECIALLY SINCE IT APPEARS TO BE INTRINSICALLY ILLEGAL...

GOD— I LOOKED LIKE SUCH A _DORK!_ IT'S ALL DUMB CLETUS'S FAULT!

HOW IS IT _HIS_ FAULT?

THERE MUST BE SOME WAY TO MAKE HIM _PAY_ FOR MY HUMILIATION!

AND WHAT BETTER WAY COULD THERE BE TO INFLICT SUFFERING THAN TO TAKE AWAY THE WOMAN HE LOVES?

I _NEVER_ SLEPT WITH THEM OTHER WIMMEN, DURLAH! I SWEAR!

THAT'S NOT WHAT _BOB_ TOLD ME!

I JUST COULDN'T KEEP LYING TO HER, CLETUS...

33

BOB THE ANGRY FLOWER

HE WALKS BESIDE ME

OH, I KNOW WHAT YOU'RE THINKING— "BOB, YOU CAN'T FLY A COMMERCIAL AIRLINER! YOU'LL KILL US ALL!"

BUT DON'T FORGET FOLKS—I'VE GOT JESUS AS MY CO-PILOT!

SO EVERYBODY JUST QUIET DOWN BACK THERE AND WE'LL ALL ENJOY THE RIDE!

SUDDENLY! SOMETHING BLOWS UP!

BLAM!

JESUS! I'M STUCK! TAKE THE CONTROLS!

JESUS! THE CONTROLS!

Jesus?

are you there?

were you ever there?

BRIGHT LIGHT!

JESUS SAVES— THE AIRPLANE!

NOOOOM!

THAT'S M'BOY!

YEAH!

THAT WAS CLOSE!

35

35

BOB THE ANGRY FLOWER

BEES AND BOB DON'T MIX, ODDLY ENOUGH

THE THEORY IS RATHER SIMPLE...

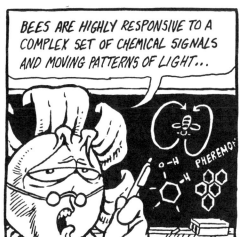

BEES ARE HIGHLY RESPONSIVE TO A COMPLEX SET OF CHEMICAL SIGNALS AND MOVING PATTERNS OF LIGHT...

PHEREMO

THUS, BY CONTROLLING THESE SIGNALS, I CAN TRANSFORM THIS SWARM OF SUPERSONIC HYPER-BEES INTO A WEAPON OF MASS DESTRUCTION!!

OH YEAH – THAT COULD NEVER GO WRONG...

BOOM! BOOM! BOOM! BOOM!

AND WHAT'S THAT SUPPOSED TO MEAN?

BZZZZZ

THOUGH I GUESS THERE COULD BE PROBLEMS IF THERE WERE ANY FLOWERS AROUND...

AAAA!

BEES!

WAIT! THEY'RE NOT STINGING! THEY JUST WANT... MY PEN?

THE BEES COLLABORATE ON A MODERN NOVEL!

THE CRITICS LOVE IT, BUT MOST READERS REJECT THE BOOK AS AN EMPTY EXERCISE IN STYLE!

THIS BEE BOOK IS REALLY LAME...

THE LOCUST BOOK WAS WAY BETTER...

BUZZ

BOB THE ANGRY **FLOWER**

IN WHICH BOB GOES TO NEW YORK AND TAKES IN A NEIL SIMON PLAY AFTER BEATING UP U.N. SECRETARY-GENERAL KOFI ANNAN!

www.compusmart.ab.ca/ snotley/ bob.htm

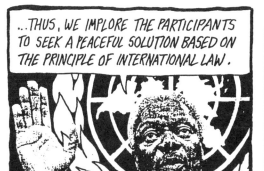

...THUS, WE IMPLORE THE PARTICIPANTS TO SEEK A PEACEFUL SOLUTION BASED ON THE PRINCIPLE OF INTERNATIONAL LAW.

HEY, KOFI! **GUT SHOT!**

OOG!

MAN, I'VE STILL GOT, LIKE, THREE HOURS TO KILL! WHAT'S THERE TO DO IN NEW YORK CITY?

...OOooOOooOh...my stomach...

MARQUEE

Ave BROADWAY

A PLAY BY Neil Simon "KILL ME NOW, I'M JUST NOT FUNNY"

YES!

HA HA HAR HAR HA HA HA HA HA HA HA HA

STOP IT! STOP IT! YOU'RE KILLING ME!

...AAAH, NEIL...

SO HOW WAS NEW YORK?

EH... KIND OF PREDICTABLE, ACTUALLY...

The Daily Post

WW III STARTS
UN SEC-GEN PUNCHED

BOB THE ANGRY FLOWER

A CHRISTMAS MYSTERY

www.compusmart.ab.ca/ snotley/ bob.htm

WHO LEFT THE FOOTPRINTS OF BIG BOOTED FEET?

WHO FILLED THE STOCKINGS WITH GOOD THINGS TO EAT?

WHO WRAPPED THE PRESENTS WITH RIBBONS SO BRIGHT?

WHO CAME TO OUR HOUSE ON THIS COLD CHRISTMAS NIGHT?

WAS IT JOLLY ST. NICK WHO LEFT US THIS SIGN?

OR A BEAST OF PURE HATRED WITH PURPOSE MALIGN?

DIE HELL-SPAWN!!!

SCREEEEE!

WOW... THAT'S NOT SANTA...

NO, IT'S NOT... FUNNY HOW THAT TURNED OUT...

38

BOB THE AN GRY FLO WER

KARAOKE CRACKER

"..MAH AKEY-BRAKEY *HART*..."

SING YOU IDIOT

MAN-THIS GUY'S TERRIBLE!

I'LL TAKE CARE OF HIM!

HI – MY NAME'S PAUL FROM EMI, AND I HAVE GOT TO GET YOU INTO A STUDIO!

AWESOME!

PRESENTLY...

THIS DOESN'T LOOK LIKE A RECORDING STUDIO...

SAY – YOU'RE NOT THINKING OF SHOOTING ME EXECUTION-STYLE FOR BEING A BAD KARAOKE SINGER, ARE YOU?

SHUT UP.

TERROR LOOSENS HIS VOICE!

PLEASE DON'T KILL ME

LIKE AN ANGEL!

BARTH GROOKS Don't Kill Me

BARTH GROOKS a DON'T KILL ME CHRISTMAS

#1!

HE BECOMES A SUCCESSFUL COUNTRY AND WESTERN STAR!

AND BOB BECOMES HIS MANAGER!

YOU JUST KEEP RIGHT ON SINGING THERE, MISTER COWBOY...

NOTLEY '98 1-5

BOB THE ANGRY FLOWER

THUS SPAK ZARATHUSTRA

MAN—I FEEL EMPTY! I GUESS I'D BETTER GET A RELIGION... EXCEPT—THERE'S SO MANY! HOW CAN I POSSIBLY CHOOSE?

zoril /zor-il/ *n.* a Japanese...
zoril /zur-il/ *n.* a flesh-eating African mammal of the skunk and weasel family.
Zoroastrianism /like it sounds/ *n.* the dualistic religious system taught by Zarathustra based on the concept of a conflict between a spirit of light and a spirit of darkness.
zounds /zounds/ *int. archaic.* expressing surprise or indignation.
zucchetto /zu-chet-oh/ *n.* Roman Catholic ecclesiastic's skullcap

HELLO— WHAT'S THIS?

SOON...

NOW YOU'RE A ZOROASTRIAN!

AND...

WISE LORD AHURA-MAZDA HEAR MY PRAYER

WISE LORD! A PRAYER!

GET OUT— REALLY?

UNIVERSE 9:NE2

I DIDN'T BELIEVE IT EITHER—BUT THERE IT IS!

WOW... DOES THAT EVER TAKE ME BACK...

PLEEZ PLEEZ

MAGNIFICATION: 100000000000000000000000X

HECK—THAT MAKES MY DAY! GO AHEAD, PHIL—GIVE HIM WHATEVER HE'S ASKING FOR!

GD LVS ME

BOB THE ANGRY FLOWER

SEVEN MINUTES IN TIBET

APPROACHING TARGET...LOOKING FOR VISUAL CONFIRMATION...

GOT HIM...OKAY, HOLD 'ER STEADY...I'M GOING DOWN...

ALL RIGHT, YOU FREAKY OLD GURU — TELL ME HOW TO FIND PEACE!

click!

TO PLUCK A SINGLE BLOSSOM IS A GLORIOUS TRAGEDY.

GOOD, GOOD... KEEP IT COMING...

HURRY IT UP, BOSS— THERE'S A BRUTAL WIND SHEAR AT THIS ALTITUDE...

JUST SHUT UP AND DO YOUR DAMN JOB!

I'VE STILL GOT NINETY MINUTES OF TAPE TO FILL, POPS, SO LET'S—

WHOOOOOSH!

YURK!

BONK! BONK! BONK!

...JUST AN AMAZING EXPERIENCE. I'VE NEVER FELT SUCH A SENSE OF SERENITY...PEACEFULNESS.

NOTLEY '98 1-17

41

BOB THE ANGRY FLOWER

THE FRAY

What politics lack these days are some obvious, direct THREATS.

Hello everyone. Vote for me or I'll blow up the entire universe.

CANDIDATE'S CORNER

So, Bob — you're in the race. Yet there's no election currently being contested.

John, the average Joe is getting damn impatient with petty special interest politics when there's an entire cosmos to be swept clean by fire.

What good are TAX CUTS in the lifeless rubble of a SHATTERED WORLD, you IGNORANT RABBLE?!?

YEAH! CLAP CLAP WOO! YES CLAP CLAP YEAH CLAP CLAP WOO! RIGHT ON! FIRE CLAP CLAP CLA WOO YES!

And then... SCANDAL!

The Daily Journal
MONDAY, JANUARY 26, 1998

BOB WON'T BLOW UP WORLD AFTER ALL
'More like an implosion' -Flower

SUN NO BLOW BOB?

TAX CUTS

RESULTS

Bitter and angry, Bob refuses to destroy the world as he had threatened to do.

KEEP YOUR PROMISE

END OUR PAIN

GET LOST!

His political credibility never recovers.

BOB THE ANGRY FLOWER

A HIGHLY QUESTIONABLE TALE FROM BOB'S PAST

HAVE YOU ALWAYS LIVED HERE, BOB?

FUNNY YOU SHOULD ASK...

STUMPY AND I BOTH ORIGINALLY CAME FROM A TINY TOWN VERY FAR AWAY FROM HERE.

ONE DAY WE WERE HELPING SOME GUY MOVE HIS JUNK...

"WE HAD JUST LOADED HIS DISHWASHER WHEN OPPORTUNITY BLEW HER BIG BRASS HORN."

KEEP AN EYE ON THIS STUFF WHILE I GO TO THE CAN, OKAY?

SURE.

"RIGHT OR WRONG, WE TOOK HIS WASHER AND HEADED FOR THE CITY."

DRIVE! **DRIVE!**

"THAT DISHWASHER WAS A GAMBLING GENIUS! IT COULD BEAT THE ODDS ON ANYTHING — WE MADE $250,000 AT THE TRACK IN ONE DAY!"

"WE PARTIED LIKE KINGS FOR WEEKS!"

"THEN THE MAFIA CAUGHT UP WITH US."

BLAM BLAM

GOSH — IS THAT WHY YOU DON'T HAVE A DISHWASHER NOW?

AMONG OTHER REASONS...

43

BOB THE ANGRY FLOWER

EVERYTHING'S OK

HEY—YOU'RE BOB THE ANGRY FLOWER! MAN, YOU'RE CRAZY!

OH YEAH, I'M CRAZY, I'M SO "NUTS"...

FOR YOUR INFORMATION, MOST MENTAL ILLNESS CAN BE CONTROLLED WITH APPROPRIATE DRUG THERAPIES!

YES, IT'S BEEN A STRUGGLE—BUT I THINK I'VE MADE A LOT OF PROGRESS! COMMENTS LIKE YOURS DON'T HELP!

SO WHAT'LL IT BE—TEN LITTLE SPIDERS OR THREE BIG ONES?

UM...TEN LITTLE ONES...I GUESS?

PFFT...AND YOU SAY I'M CRAZY?

SCRIK SCRIK

SPIDERS!

FOLKS, WHEN YOU'RE IN HIS POSITION, TRY TO THINK SENSIBLY.

SERIOUSLY—THREE BIG SPIDERS ARE WAY EASIER TO HANDLE THAN TEN LITTLE ONES...

C'MON, PEOPLE... IT'S OBVIOUS...

TAP TAP

At least that's what the SPIDERS tell me...

44

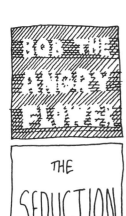

THE
SEDUCTION

Shhh! WE DON'T WANT TO WAKE ANYBODY UP!

OKAY... WHOOPS! ≩giggle!≩

MMMMMM

MMMMM

SO...WHERE'S THE BEDROOM?

YES YES YES

RIGHT THIS WAY, DARLIN'...

NOW, IT'S A LITTLE MESSY...

ZOOM!

ZOOM!

ZOOM!

SOMEHOW I SCARE AWAY THE GOOD ONES, STUMPY...

BOB THE ANGRY FLOWER

SAYONARA SUN

WELL, FOLKS, I GUESS THIS IS GOODBYE, HERE...

BUT BEFORE I GO, A WORD OF THANKS TO **SUN** EDITORS **NEAL WATSON** AND **ERIK FLOREN**. GREAT GUYS, BOTH OF THEM, AND THEY DESERVE BETTER THAN A PAIR OF BADLY REFERENCED CARICATURES OF THEM WEARING SUPERMAN OUTFITS, BUT LIFE IS PAINFULLY UNFAIR THAT WAY.

NEAL! ERIK!

IT'S ALSO BEEN A PLEASURE SHARING A PAGE WITH STEVE "DENIM MAN/ALTERNATIVE LAMENT COLUMNIST" TILLEY.

SORRY, BUDDY, NO CAN DO. I ONLY WEAR DENIM.

AH, BUT THIS **IS** DENIM! SOFT, BLACK, NEW DENIM!

Steve TILLEY
ALTERNATIVE LAMENT

JUST TO BE CLEAR, FOLKS—STEVE DOESN'T REALLY WEAR DENIM ALL THE TIME. THAT WAS JUST A JOKE.

ISN'T THAT RIGHT, STEVE?

YEAH, IT WAS HILARIOUS. I'M **STILL** HEARING ABOUT THAT...

SECURITY
GRIB IZOW SKI
SUN
SECURITY
ROSS

SO, ANYWAY, IT'S BEEN A BALL, BUT I GOTTA RUN...

SUN
BOOT!

MEANWHILE, IN REALITY...

OKAY, SO IT'S A... IT'S A FLOWER THAT TALKS?

scratch

I GUESS...

SUN
OH MY GOD!

THANKS. PAUL.

SN

To the Journal

While the *Sun* was great, it had started to bother me that nobody I knew read my cartoon any more. I mean, I knew *somebody* was reading it, but none of my peers seemed to read the *Sun*, so all of these brilliant cartoons were being read by my mother and thousands of other people but not the people who I wanted to see it, i.e. my friends. So when the *Edmonton Journal* came along and expressed interest in running Bob, I jumped at the chance. The *Sun* had a reputation for being a redneck-y kind of tabloid, whereas the *Journal* was the bigger paper, considered to be Edmonton's paper of record. I figured that Bob's audience would have a better chance of being *Journal* readers.

Hardly. As far as I've been able to tell, my peers don't read either paper. Of course, I didn't know that at the time, so with an in-joke-filled final flourish, I bid adieu to the *Sun* and jumped over to the competition. The first *Journal* cartoon, "Why We Have Unions," was both a straighforward description of the jump and a small gesture of scrappiness intended to arouse to ire of Conrad Black, the union-hating owner of the Southam newspaper chain. Totally unnoticed, of course.

I'd never experienced censorship at the *Sun*, but that was to change at the *Journal*. First they refused to run "Gornar," then they insisted that I change "Rock Climbing." To their credit, however, they did run "Talibantastic" and "Bought," both of which resulted in wonderful, wonderful letters complaining about my cartoon. Keep 'em coming!

I continue to probe the boundaries of what I can get away with at the *Journal*.

BOB THE ANGRY FLOWER

WHY WE HAVE UNIONS

SO YOU'RE OFFERING $200 A MONTH WITH NO BENEFITS, NO HEALTH CARE, NO DENTAL— NO *NOTHING?*

THAT'S RIGHT.

I'M GOING TO HAVE TO THINK ABOUT IT...

TAKE A WEEK.

AND SO BOB THINKS...

...AND THINKS...

HARDER! *HARDER!!!*

...AND THINKS.

WHAT DO *YOU* THINK I SHOULD DO?

SO? WHAT DID YOU DECIDE?

WELL, HERE'S MY COUNTER-PROPOSAL...

1. I WANT AN $8000 HANG-GLIDING ALLOWANCE.

2. I NEED A GUY TO CRUSH MY HAND IN A VICE EVERY WEEK.

3. I REQUIRE A TOTAL BAN ON THE CONSUMPTION OF BEEF ANYWHERE IN THE BUILDING.

NOTLEY '98 2-27

NO, NO, AND NO.

IT'S A DEAL!

BOB THE ANGRY FLOWER

AH, WINSTON... HOW THE HECK ARE YOU GOING TO GET OUT OF THIS ONE?

OUT OF NOWHERE I APPEAR—THE WISH TURTLE! I CAN GRANT YOU ANY WISH—ANYTHING!

REALLY?

PZONG!

OKAY—GIMME A HUGE TURKISH WARRIOR WITH A GIANT SCIMITAR AND A TURBAN WITH A BIG SPIKE IN IT AND WHO ANSWERS ONLY TO THE NAME "PAUL DONUT-BAXTER"!!!

YOU CAN TAKE MORE TIME TO THINK ABOUT IT, YOU KNOW...

C'MON, WISHY—LET'S GO!

SNAP! SNAP!

DOINK!

MR. DONUT-BAXTER?

HEY—CALL ME PAUL.

AND SO A CRIMEFIGHTING TEAM WAS BORN!

HE'S A TURK!

AND HE'S A FLOWER!

TOGETHER, THEY ARE

H.A.R.D. F.O.R.C.E.

49

THE ANGRY FLOWER

SUPPOSING BOB LIVED IN AN EVIL MONARCHY...

OMIGOSH! IT'S THE KING!

WHAT—HERE? NOW?

A SALAD IN TEN SECONDS OR IT'S OFF WITH YOUR HEADS!

ZOOM!

EIGHT SECONDS LATER...

ZIP!!

YOUR SALAD, SIRE!

crunch... crunch

THIS IS AWFUL!! YOU DARE SERVE THIS TO YOUR KING??

OKAY, YES, GRANTED — IT'S NOT SO MUCH A SALAD AS IT IS A PILE OF CHOPPED LETTUCE WITH SOME KETCHUP SQUIRTED IN IT — BUT COME ON! YOU ONLY GAVE US TEN SECONDS! NOBODY COULD MAKE AN EDIBLE SALAD IN THAT TIME!

HEADS OFF!!

WHAT A NIGHTMARE! THANK GOD I LIVE IN A STABLE DEMOCRACY!

MMM...WHAT WAS THAT, BABY?

AAIEE!!

50

THE ANGRY FLOWER

SOME WAYS OF MAKING MONEY

IN A SECRET LOCATION, THE ELITE GATHER TO WAGER ON FORBIDDEN BLOODSPORTS.

OKAY, FOLKS, PLACE YOUR BETS...

THIS ROUND, A MONK WITH A VOW OF SILENCE TAKES ON A LUNK WITH A SOW OF VIOLENCE!!!

...RRRRR...

TEN THOUSAND ON THE PIG!

YEAH!

THAT'S A MEAN-LOOKING PIG!

NOBODY WANTS TO BET ON MR. QUIET? HE HASN'T SAID A WORD IN 17 YEARS — I THINK HE'S GOT A LOT OF FRUSTRATION TO WORK OUT!

HE'S RIGHT!

I'D BE STEAMED!

TWENTY THOUSAND ON ST. FRANCIS!

JUST A SECOND.

HANG ON.

ONE AT A TIME.

THAT IT?

NO MORE BETS?

then... FIGHT!

SECONDS LATER...

OW! I GIVE UP! MERCY!!

THAT WAS QUICK.

HE'S TALKING PLENTY NOW...

HEY—WHERE'D THAT FLOWER GO WITH THE MONEY?!?

HE'S INVESTING IT WISELY— IN MUTUAL FUNDS!!!

I ADVISE SELECTING A RANGE OF FUNDS...

UH-HUH...

NOTLEY '98 2-28

IT'S BEEN WEEKS WITH NO SIGN OF RESCUE... WE'RE COMPLETELY OUT OF FOOD.

EVERYBODY'S THINKING THE SAME THING, BUT NOBODY WANTS TO BE THE FIRST TO SAY IT OUT LOUD.

BUT SOMEBODY HAS TO SAY IT, SO I'LL SAY IT.

WE'RE GOING TO HAVE TO EAT THE DEAD.

WHOA! *TIME OUT!* MAYBE YOU PEOPLE WILL HAVE TO EAT THE DEAD!

I'M A *PLANT!* ALL I NEED IS WATER AND A SUNNY DAY!!!

WOW - KIND OF A NIGHTMARE FOR YOU GUYS, THOUGH... THANK GOD I WON'T HAVE TO COMMIT SUCH A SICKENING, UNFORGIVABLE CRIME!

And every single one of you EVIL inhuman MONSTERS is heading STRAIGHT TO HELL for it, too.

WELL — I'M GOING SKIING!

NOT TWO DAYS LATER...

C'MON... GIMME SOME!

NO.

BOB THE ANGRY FLOWER

empathy

HEY, BOB—DID YOU JUST TAKE THIS KID'S LOLLIPOP?

YEAH—SO WHAT?

HOW WOULD YOU FEEL IF THE SAME THING HAPPENED TO YOU?

JEEZ—I DON'T KNOW! LET ME GO CHECK.

MORAL REPERCUSSION CHAMBER

CAUTION

PSH!

OKAY, FREDDIE, FIRE IT UP!

YESSIR!

PROPS

GIVE ME YOUR <object> LOLLIPOP <object>

CLANK CLANK

PUSH

TAKE

SEQUENCE COMPLETE

HMMM...

Y'KNOW, IT WOULDN'T REALLY BOTHER ME...

53

Big Scary Block

So everything was skipping along just fine at the *Journal*, except that it really wasn't. The cartoons that had appeared in the *Journal* were ones I'd drawn while Bob was still running in the *Sun*, and even though that shouldn't have made a difference, for some reason it did. I did "Empathy," and then next week came "Mystery Moon Monster P.I." Everything seemed fine until I finished the cartoon, and then I panicked. It was completely nonsensical! I'd lost it! I couldn't draw cartoons any more! For the first time I'd gotten right to the end of a cartoon and realized it was unsuitable for publication.

In truth, it wasn't that bad, especially in the context of some of the material I've had the audacity to be paid for since. But for some reason all the nervousness of the move to the *Journal*, combined with the lingering stress of publishing the first Bob book *In Defence of Fascism*, came together and locked up my cartoon judgment circuits.

It was scary. I wandered the streets for hours that evening. What had gone wrong? Had I lost it for good? Eventually I stumbled into a bar, ordered some food, and wrote "Fear Soup," one of my more nakedly autobiographical cartoons. Weirdly, that seemed to do the trick... for about two weeks, when I froze again.. This time the semi-autobiographical solution was "Putting His Affairs In Order," which really did do the trick this time by suddenly opening my eyes to the fun of screwing around with panel layout. Freedom!

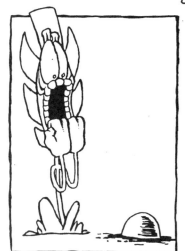

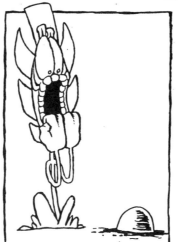

BOB THE ANGRY FLOWER

BY THIS HAND BETRAYED

HEY! BOB!

HUH? WHO SAID THAT?

I DID!

BUT—YOU'RE MY HAND!

or leaf or whatever it is...

THAT'S RIGHT! I CAN TALK!

OH YEAH... YOU'VE GOT A LITTLE MOUTH AND EVERYTHING...

AND YOU, BOB, ARE FEELING VERRRY SLEEEEPY... SOON YOU'RE TUMBLING, TUMBLING INTO A DEEP DREAMLESS SLUMBER...

WOW... FAST ASLEEP...

WHAT A SUCKER!

Z.

A FEW DAYS LATER BOB IS PLAYING SOME POKER WITH THE FUTURE PEOPLE WHO LOOK CHINESE BUT HAVE BIG GOOFY AFROS.

SO, BOB—WASN'T THAT YOUR HAND READING THE SIX O'CLOCK NEWS ON T.V. WHILE YOU WERE ASLEEP?

NO! LIES! I CONTROL MY HAND! ME!!!

BUT HIS MIND IS PLAGUED BY DOUBTS...

HOW CAN I EVER BE SURE?

CAN'T TRUST HIS OWN HAND—MAN, THAT'S A TOUGH ONE!

BOB THE ANGRY FLOWER

THE PRECIPICE

WELL, I'M IN A HECK OF A FIX, HERE...

IT'S MY BIG TRAPEZE NUMBER, BUT MY ENEMIES HAVE STOLEN THE SAFETY NET AND RIGGED THE SWING WITH BANANAS THAT COULDN'T POSSIBLY SUPPORT MY WEIGHT...

I MUST REMEMBER MY OLD TEACHER'S ADVICE.

YOU GOTTA KNOW WHEN TO HOLD 'EM
KNOW WHEN TO FOLD 'EM
KNOW WHEN TO WALK AWAY
KNOW WHEN TO RUN

UH-HUH

YEP!

RIGHT!

GOT IT

THIS IS GREAT STUFF, KENNY— PURE GOLD. NOW, ABOUT THOSE BANANA TRAPEZES — WHAT SHOULD I DO IF I RUN INTO ONE OF THEM?

KENNY?

KENNY!

I GUESS I'M ON MY OWN.

KENNY, IF YOU'RE OUT THERE SOME- WHERE... THIS ONE'S FOR YOU.

FOR THE GAMBLER!

SNAP!

DAMN YOU, KENNY.

THUD!

NOTLEY '98 4-24

Bob The Angry Flower
· THE FACILITIES ·

THIS PLACE IS A DUMP!

BUT THE BATHROOMS—? SURPRISINGLY TIDY!

YEAH, *SURE*...

IT'S TRUE... ALL POLISHED MARBLE AND SMOOTH SILVER FIXTURES... CHOPIN PLAYS LIGHTLY FROM HIDDEN SPEAKERS WHILE THE AIR IS SOFT WITH THE MEREST HINT OF ROSE...

YEAH, RIGHT! MIND IF I SEE FOR MY<u>SELF</u>?

BE MY GUEST!

...WOW...

I CAN'T BELIEVE IT! AMAZING!

AND DID YOU HAPPEN TO NOTICE THE ENCHANTED MIRROR FULL OF MONSTERS?

NOTICE THE WHAT?

AIEE!

CRASH! GROBBLE!

HEH HEH...

ENERMIES LIST
~~John Denver~~
~~Lady Di~~
~~Mr. Skeptic~~
Tim Woodsman
Invisible Cow

NOT LONG AFTER...

OH, SURE—THE PLACE IS A DUMP—BUT YOU SHOULD SEE THE <u>CAN</u>!

BOB THE ANGRY FLOWER

Light Amplification by the Stimulated Emission of Radiation

SO YOU'RE SELLING ALL YOUR STUFF...

UH-HUH. TAX BILL.

SO DOES THAT INCLUDE—

...MY HEAD-MOUNTED LASER? OH, YES...

...THOUGH I STILL LOVE YOU, BABY...

KISS KISS.

"I GUESS WE'LL BE HEARING FROM KEVIN "LASERS" BOWMAN, THEN."

...SO YOU'RE FINALLY SELLING IT, HUH? FOR REAL THIS TIME?

YEP.

I GOT HAND LASERS, LEG LASERS, GROIN LASERS — BUT I STILL ALWAYS DREAMED OF ONE DAY WEARING THE CROWN!

zap!

THIS IS THE BEST DAY OF MY LIFE!

ZAP!

ACTUALLY, KEV — I'M AFRAID I'VE ALREADY SOLD IT!

WHAT?

NO WAY!

WHO TO?

LOUISE THE HEADLESS OLD LADY???

AW JEEZ!

C'MON!

SHE DOESN'T NEED IT!

 **BOB THE ANGRY FLOWER** — coping

WHAT'S UP, BOB?

I JUST GOT AN AWESOME JOB HERE AT GUILLOTINE GLASS!!

GUILLOTINE GLASS INC.

ONE TRANSPARENTLY FORESHADOWED MISHAP LATER...

BONK!...

SOON...

OOOOH... MY HEAD... WHA... WHA' HAPPEN?

GOOD NEWS, MR. FLOWER!

WE WERE ABLE TO ATTACH YOUR HEAD TO A COPY OF J.D. SALINGER'S _CATCHER IN THE RYE_!

IT'S A CLASSIC!

THE NEWS IS SO HORRIFYING THAT BOB BLACKS OUT AND DREAMS OF MOIST, DELICIOUS SUSHI FOR FIVE MINUTES!

SAKE (SALMON)

MAGURO (TUNA)

KAPPA MAKI (CUCUMBER ROLL)

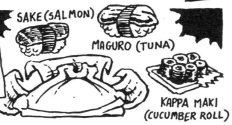

THEN:

YOU PUT MY HEAD ON A _BOOK_? LOOK AT ME!! YOU'VE MADE ME INTO SOME KIND OF _FREAK_!

WHAT—MORE OF A FREAK THAN BEING A BIG TALKING FLOWER?

FRANKLY, YES.

THERE IS AN UP SIDE, HOWEVER...

SAY—HAVE YOU EVER READ _CATCHER IN THE RYE_?

AS A MATTER OF FACT...

WINONA RYDER

BOB THE ANGRY FLOWER

YES YOU CAN

www.compusmart.ab.ca/snotley/bob.htm

SADDLE UP, BOYS! TIME FOR A FIELD TRIP TO THE CANNERY!

CANZ

...AND THEN THE CAN CONVEYOR CARRIES THE CANS TO THE CAN CATCHER, AND THAT'S WHERE THE CANS ARE FILLED WITH ALL THE WONDERFUL THINGS YOU CAN BUY IN CANS!

OH I SEE.

SIMPLE IF YOU THINK ABOUT IT...

YAWN...

AUTHORIZED PERSONNEL ONLY

NO ADMITTANC

OH MY GOD — LOVE! CASES OF IT!!

LOVE

I KNEW IT WAS OUT THERE SOMEWHERE!

THAT'S RIGHT!

LOVE! ™

THAT MOST PRECIOUS HUMAN CONNECTION, NOW AVAILABLE AS A MUSHY PINK PASTE FROM A CAN! BUY IT AND FIND OUT WHAT YOU'VE BEEN MISSING!

I'M SO HAPPY!

65

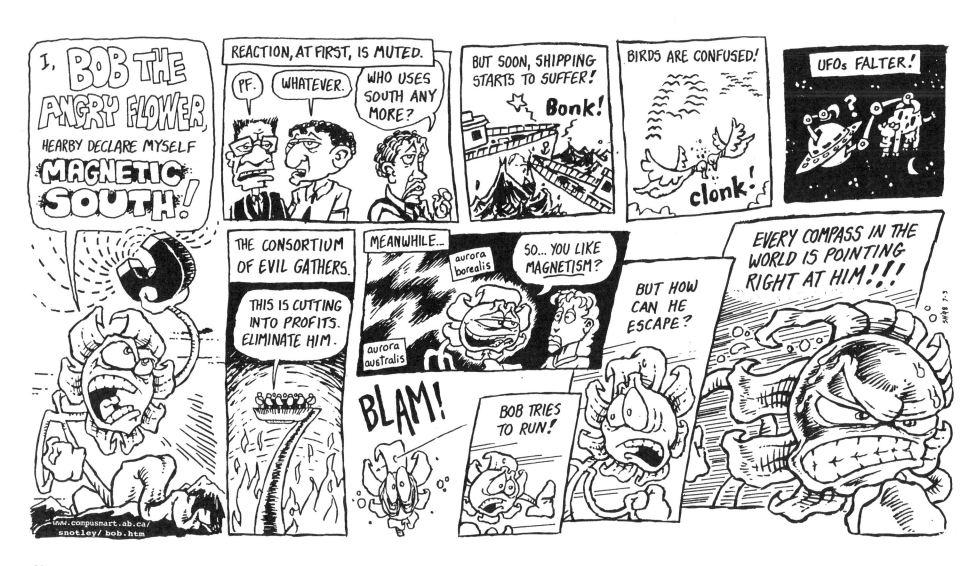

IN A SPLIT SECOND EACH OF OUR HEROES RELIVES HIS PROFOUNDEST REGRET!

BOB THE ANGRY **FLOWER**

APPEARANCES CAN BE DEAD ON

www.compusmart.ab.ca/snotley/bob.htm

HA HA HA! ONE MORE BLAST FROM THE UGLY RAY AND YOU'RE FINISHED!

...please...

...no more...

YES MORE!

BLORK!!

WHAT THE...

OOOH...

WHAT HAVE YOU DONE? NOW I LOOK LIKE SARAH MICHELLE GELLAR FROM TV'S BUFFY THE VAMPIRE SLAYER!!!

THE UGLY RAY HAS MADE HIM SO UGLY HE'S BEAUTIFUL! HOW CAN THIS BE??

BOB GOES ON A LECTURE TOUR!

JUST WHAT IS THE UGLY RAY TRYING TO TELL US?

BUT WAIT!

WHAT'S THIS?

HAS BOB BEEN TIED UP AND REPLACED BY AN IMPOSTER?

NO — IT'S JUST A CARDBOARD CUTOUT. FALSE ALARM, FOLKS...

SO YOU BUILT THE UGLY RAY OUT OF SHAME OVER YOUR OWN APPEARANCE?

THAT WAS CERTAINLY A BIG PART OF IT, BOB...

TALK BACK

BOB THE ANGRY FLOWER

TALIBAN-TASTIC!

WHAT'S WITH THE TURBAN?

SILENCE, INFIDEL!!

I JUST GOT PERMISSION FROM AFGHANISTAN TO SET UP A LOCAL CHAPTER OF THE *TALIBAN!*

WE'LL DEPOSE THE GOVERNMENT AND BRING IN A CRUEL AND OPPRESSIVE REGIME WHERE MUSIC, DANCING AND FUN ARE FORBIDDEN IN AN INSANELY STRICT READING OF ISLAMIC LAW!

SO WHAT DO YOU DO AFTER HOURS, THEN?

TABLE TENNIS!

IT'S A FAST-PACED AND EXCITING GAME THAT ANYBODY CAN PLAY WITHOUT OFFENDING THE JOY-HATING HOLY GAZE OF ALLAH!!

YOU PLAY **PING-PONG?**

NO...WE PLAY TABLE TENNIS

INFIDEL...

THERE'S A DIFFERENCE.

AND SO WE PROCEED TO THE WORLD TABLE TENNIS FINALS...

WELL, JIM, THE TALIBAN TEAM'S CRUEL AND OPPRESSIVE STYLE IS REALLY PAYING OFF FOR THEM!

YOU SAID IT IT, FRANK...

GAH!

ALLAH GRANTS THEM THE CUP!

WHERE IS YOUR VEIL, WHORE?

71

BOB THE ANGRY FLOWER

EVERYBODY LOVES JELLO

THEY'LL BE WITH YOU IN A MOMENT, MR. FLOWER.

THANK YOU.

RECEPTION

INVEST CORP.

OKAY, BOB, YOU'VE BEEN PRACTISING THIS PRESENTATION FOR A MONTH — SO DON'T BLOW IT!

AT THIS POINT GOD ROLLS A 38 ON THE WANDERING MONSTER TABLE...

A GELATINOUS CUBE !!!

CUBE!

SQUIRP!

THEY'RE READY FOR YOU NOW, MR. FLOWER.

CUBE!

THINGS START TO MOVE PRETTY QUICKLY, NOW!

BOB SELLS THE BOARD ON HIS PRODUCT PLAN!

THEY HAVE A WORKING PROTOTYPE IN UNDER THREE MONTHS!

BUY

BOLD ADVERTISING WINS THEM A 15% MARKET SHARE!

LOCAL ADVENTURERS DEAL WITH THE GELATINOUS CUBE.

MELGRIM! THE FIRE SPELL!

CUBE!

NOTLEY '98

MAYOR, COUNCILLORS — THIS CITY'S A SHAMBLES! BASIC SERVICES ARE CRUMBLING BECAUSE OF THIS COUNCIL'S TOTAL FIXATION ON ONE CIVIC ISSUE TO THE EXCLUSION OF ALL OTHERS!

NOW... CAN ANY OF YOU TELL ME WHAT THAT ISSUE IS?

BRAINS!

BRAINS!

BRAINS!

YES...

BRAINS...

I KNOW — EATING BRAINS IS THE ONLY WAY TO EASE THE PAIN OF BEING DEAD. BUT LET'S WIDEN OUR FOCUS...

BRAAAINS

BRAAINS...

WE HAVE TO THINK OUTSIDE THE BOX, HERE, PEOPLE...

DOES ANYONE HERE HAVE ANY NEW IDEAS?

BRAAINS

B

BLAM

BRAI...

AND DON'T SAY BRAINS!

HMMMMMM...

TAX HIKE?

I SAID OUTSIDE THE BOX, PEOPLE!

73

BOB THE ANGRY FLOWER

TIME FOR SOME NEW FRIENDS

YOU'RE HERE ABOUT THE AD? GREAT! COME ON IN!

NOW, ANYBODY WHO WANTS TO BE MY NEW FRIEND HAS TO BEAT ME AT GO —AND I WARN YOU, I'M PRETTY DARN GOOD!!

GO IS AN ANCIENT CHINESE GAME IN WHICH THE PIECES (OR "STONES") ARE PUT ON THE BOARD SUCH THAT THEY SPELL OUT THE WORD "GO"!

GO Victory!

Bitter, shameful defeat!

THIS ISN'T HOW YOU PLAY GO...

GET OUT!!

DIFFERENT APPLICANTS COME AND "GO" ALL DAY LONG!

WHOSE GAME IS THIS, ANYWAY?

NO, I DON'T NEED THE INSTRUCTIONS!

DO YOU WANNA BE MY FRIEND OR NOT?

NEXT!

GUESS WE'LL HAVE TO STICK WITH THE OLD FRIENDS!

YAY!

!

74

BOB THE ANGRY FLOWER

DIPLOMACY

www.compusmart.ab.ca/snotley/bob.htm

81

...YOU HAVE ONE HOUR TO COMPLY.

OKAY—THE U.N. KNOWS WE MEAN BUSINESS!

I'D SAY WE'VE GOT HALF AN HOUR BEFORE *CAPTAIN JUSTICE* OR *LUGOR* PUNCHES HIS WAY THROUGH THAT DOOR!

NOW, SOME OF YOU HAVE EXPRESSED CONCERNS ABOUT MY *ESCAPE ROCKET.*

MAX: 1 FLOWER

APPARENTLY SOME OF YOU THINK I'M PLANNING ON *DUCKING OUT* AT THE FIRST SIGN OF *TROUBLE!*

YOU PEOPLE AREN'T JUST *HENCHMEN* OR *UNDERLINGS* TO ME... YOU'RE *FAMILY.* I RESPECT YOU TOO MUCH TO THROW YOU AWAY BY THE DOZEN AS CANNON FODDER. WE'RE IN THIS *TOGETHER!*

snif snif   snif   snif

AND TO PROVE IT, THIS IS THE ROCKET'S CODE KEY!

HURRAH!

MEANWHILE, FAR AWAY IN COMPLETE SAFETY...

NOW—BATTLE STATIONS!

NOW—BATTLE STATIONS!

ROBOT ME

82

BOB THE ANGRY FLOWER

BUILDING THE PERFECT PSYCHIC DUMMY HEAD

I'VE DECIDED TO TAKE A SECOND LOOK AT SOME PROJECTS I'D GIVEN UP ON!

OH?

REMEMBER THIS ONE? THE PSYCHIC DUMMY HEAD? YOU WERE SO CERTAIN I WAS CRAZY!

UM...

THIS STUPID THING CAN'T TELL THE FUTURE AT ALL!!!

WHY? WHY? WHY?

CURSE YOU!

...SURE...

I WAS CLOSE, I KNOW IT... JUST SOME MISSING ELEMENT...

GIVE IT UP, MAN. I TOLD YOU IT WASN'T GOING TO WORK...

LIGHT CONE

SO YOU DID... SOMEHOW... YOU KNEW THE FUTURE!

IF YOU'VE GOT SOME DUMB BRAIN-SWITCH IDEA, YOU CAN FORGET IT...

COMPLETELY, TOTALLY, UNEQUIVOCABLY CAUGHT IN HIS TERRIBLE CONTEMPLATION

DIDN'T I SAY HE WAS GOING TO TRY AGAIN?

THANKS FOR THE WARNING, MAN...THAT'S ANOTHER ONE I OWE YOU...

BOB THE ANGRY FLOWER!

HOW DO YOU...LIKE... COME UP WITH THIS STUFF?

IT'S ALL OVER

CHIPS!

crunch gorge

CHIPZ BBQ

...ooOooOoh...

CHIPZ BBQ

Hilarious Idea

REPEAT UNTIL DEAD

86

BOB THE ANGRY FLOWER

LAZ

MACHINE THAT SPITS OUT CASH! YOU JUST HAVE TO PRESS THESE TWO BUTTONS

crinch cronch

LATER:

HEY—I NEED FIVE BUCKS!

WHAT?

Stuff! $5

WHAT ABOUT THAT MONEY MACHINE??

eh... ...I PUSHED ONE OF THE BUTTONS AND NOTHING HAPPENED...

STUPID THING...WHY SHOULD YOU HAVE TO HIT ANY BUTTONS?? WHY NOT A TIMER? THEN YOU'D JUST HAVE MONEY WAITING FOR YOU EVERY MORNING!

STUMPY INDIGNANTLY SENDS BOB HOME TO GET HIS OWN DAMN MONEY...

ONCE THERE, SHEER LAZINESS DENIES BOB THE VICTORY!

89

BOB THE ANGRY FLOWER

AN ADDITION TO MY WAY OF THINKING

HEY, FREDDIE — C'MERE...

I'M HYPNOTISING MYSELF, AND I NEED YOU TO GIVE ME THESE SUGGESTIONS WHEN I'M UNDER!

1: You are thin.

2: You look great.

3: You live in a castle with robot servants.

I'LL BE AN EMPEROR IN THE WORLD OF MY OWN PERCEPTIONS!

WHY DOESN'T EVERY-BODY DO THIS?!?

WHY ASK ME? WHY NOT ASK STUMPY?

STUMPY? IN MY SUB-CONSCIOUS? HE'S MY CLOSEST FRIEND — HE'D RIP ME APART!

WHEREAS YOUR SMALL-MINDED FEARS AND LIMITATIONS WILL KEEP YOU HONEST!

Zoink!

SMALL-MINDED, HUH? I'LL SHOW HIM!

LATER, IN BOB'S MIND:

HMM... I DON'T REMEMBER GETTING THAT PAINTING...

CONFERENCE

GENTLEMEN, PLEASE TAKE YOUR SEATS.

SOME OF YOU ARE *ELEPHANTS*, SOME OF YOU ARE *SHEEP*, SOME OF YOU ARE *CROCODILES*... AND YET, DESPITE THOSE DIFFERENCES, THERE IS ONE THING THAT UNITES YOU ALL: BEING *ANIMALS*, YOU LACK THE CAPACITY TO UNDERSTAND ANY OF WHAT I'VE JUST SAID.

...sigh...

Y'KNOW, WHAT THE HELL'S THE POINT OF HAVING THIS **COUNCIL OF ANIMALS** IF NOBODY'S GOING TO *PARTICIPATE* ???

I'M OUT *THERE* BUSTING MY *ASS* FOR YOU PEOPLE, AND DO I GET *ANY* FEEDBACK ??

CAN'T ONE OF YOU DISPLAY AT LEAST A *FLICKER* OF SENTIENCE?

HELLO??? HELLOOO???

LATER:

APPARENTLY HE WAS *SIMULTANEOUSLY* ATTACKED BY DOZENS OF DIFFERENT ANIMALS...

96

THE ANGRY FLOWER

THE DIFFERENCE BEING

rustle...

7:27ᴀ

BEEP! BEEP! KRK BEEP!

DAMN!

WHA-?

7:28ᴀ

HEY! ARE YOU GUYS TRYING TO REPLACE ME WITH AN *EXACT* COPY WITH IDENTICAL MEMORIES???

CLICK!

NO!

OF COURSE NOT!

WHERE'D YOU GET THAT IDEA?

WELL, THAT'S THE DUPLICATE ME...

...THAT'S THE MEMORY TRANSFER DEVICE...

...AND THAT'S A WATERMELON... I DON'T QUITE GET THAT PART...

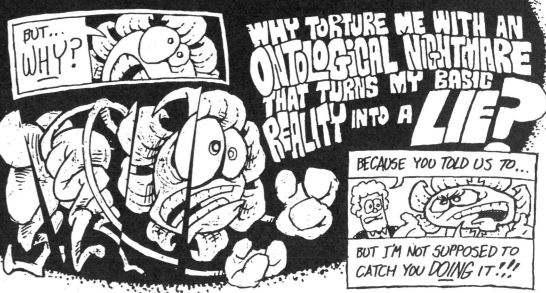

BUT... WHY?

WHY TORTURE ME WITH AN ONTOLOGICAL NIGHTMARE THAT TURNS MY BASIC REALITY INTO A LIE?

BECAUSE YOU TOLD US TO...

BUT I'M NOT SUPPOSED TO CATCH YOU *DOING* IT!!!

97

BOBTHEANGRY FLOWER

THE MIRACLE OF LIFE

"WHO'S A TINY WIDDLE-LIDDLE BABY?"

"NO... I DON'T WANT TO HEAR HOW THIS ONE IS SUPPOSED TO WORK..."

"IT'S ACTUALLY PRETTY SIMPLE!"

"BUT THEN IT HIT ME— LIFE IS SUPPOSED TO BE SHARED. IT'S ALL ABOUT GETTING CLOSER TO OTHER PEOPLE..."

"AND WHAT COULD BE MORE MEANINGFUL THAN A CONNECTION WITH A BRAND NEW PRECIOUS HUMAN LIFE?"

"ON WEDNESDAY I TOOK A GOOD HARD LOOK AT MY LIFE, AND WHAT DID I SEE? NOTHING! MY LIFE IS COMPLETELY EMPTY. AND THE MORE I TRY TO FILL IT WITH ROBOTS OR LASERS OR SICK EPISODES OF SELF-MANIPULATION, THE MORE EMPTY IT LOOKS!"

"SO YOU ADOPTED A BABY....?"

"UM... SURE... "ADOPTED"..."

100

BOB THE ANGRY FLOWER

COFFEE WITH SINISTAR

SO, YEAH, I'M WORKING FOR A GRAPHIC DESIGN COMPANY NOW...

WOW!

MAN, I'VE GOTTA SAY — YOU HAVE REALLY, REALLY CHANGED.!!

THE LAST TIME I TALKED TO YOU IT WAS JUST TWO HOURS OF YOU BELLOWING: "I **LIVE!** I **HUNGER!**"

NOW YOU'VE GOT A JOB, AND A GIRLFRIEND...

I KNOW, I KNOW...

AND TO THINK I'VE BEEN AVOIDING YOU FOR MONTHS!!!

IF YOU HADN'T CAUGHT ME ON CALL WAITING I NEVER WOULD'VE PICKED UP THE PHONE!

IN FACT, I EVEN BROUGHT A FEW SINIBOMBS, JUST IN CASE YOU WOULDN'T SHUT UP!

SINISTAR? BUDDY.? SNA-AP!

RUN, COWARD!!!

BOB THE ANGRY FLOWER

1999 MINUS 15

YOU KNEW HIM FIFTEEN YEARS AGO AS THE INESCAPABLE FACE OF AUTHORITY STARING AT YOU FROM EVERY POSTER AND VIDSCREEN. NOW HE HAS A NEW BOOK, "STILL WATCHING," AND HE JOINS US HERE TODAY. PLEASE SAY HELLO TO BIG BROTHER.

CLAP CLAP

CLAP CLAP

THANKS. THANK YOU.

CLAP CLA CLAP CL CLAP CLAP

SO.... WHERE HAVE YOU BEEN SINCE '84?

JUST BUILDING SUPPORT, BOB. MY BROADCAST IS THE THIRD HIGHEST-RATED POLITICAL SHOW IN SYNDICATION RIGHT NOW.

AND YOUR BOOK—ALREADY A BEST-SELLER.

PEOPLE TRUST ME BECAUSE I STAND FOR WHAT I ALWAYS STOOD FOR—A BOOT STAMPING ON A HUMAN FACE FOREVER.

1999 WILL BE A BIG YEAR FOR BIG BROTHER!

WE'VE PUT TOGETHER A DYNAMITE SPECIAL "THREE MINUTE HATE" EPISODE FOR SWEEPS!

WELL, THAT'S DOUBLE-PLUS-GOOD!

NOW HOW MANY FINGERS AM I HOLDING UP?

HA HA. HILARIOUS.

TAKE HIM TO ROOM 101.

109

BOB THE ANGRY FLOWER

www.compusmart.ab.ca/snotley/bob.htm

ANOTHER OUTING

GUESS WHO'S GOT THREE TICKETS TO THE *COOLEST* PLACE IN TOWN TONIGHT!

IS IT YOU?

JUST GET IN THE VAN...

AND SO...

WELCOME TO THE BORE DOME

TODAY:
HOLES
HOLES
HOLES

HM.

HMM.

HMMM...

KINDA LIMP...

LACKS INTEREST.

I DON'T GET IT—WE'RE SURROUNDED BY ALL THE *AWLS*, *AUGERS* AND *DRILLS* ANYONE COULD EVER WANT—AND YET I FIND MYSELF STRANGELY UNENTERTAINED!

HEY! YOU!

here it comes...

THIS PLACE IS *LAME!* YOU CALL IT THE *BORE DOME*, BUT ALL YOU OFFER IS *BOREDOM!*

SCREWING

A-G

G-J

WITTY.

THANKS!

BOB THE ANGRY FLOWER!

WELL, I EXPECTED THE POPE TO DIE THIS YEAR...

...AND I KINDA THOUGHT BORIS YELTSIN WOULD DIE THIS YEAR, TOO...

...BUT I NEVER THOUGHT I'D FIND THEM *BOTH* DEAD IN A *SWEATY LOUISIANA MOTEL ROOM*!!

IT'S QUITE A MYSTERY, BY GORNAR!

Did somebody mention my name?

GORNAR!

THIS CHANGES EVERYTHING! NOW YOU CAN BRING THEM BACK TO LIFE!

Well... sort of...

BACK TO LIFE... AS RABBITS!

IT'S KIND OF A FUNNY STORY...

Bob The Angry Flower in:

"Those Bongo-Playing Idiots Outside My Window"

THE THING I RESPECT MOST ABOUT THESE PEOPLE IS THE *EXTRAORDINARY* AMOUNT OF *TALENT* AND *DISCIPLINE* IT TAKES TO PLAY SOMETHING AS *COMPLEX* AS A *BONGO!*

IT'S A *RARE ARTIST* WHO HAS THE *SKILL* AND *PATIENCE* TO GET SOUND OUT OF *THAT* THING!!!

THESE GUYS AREN'T JUST *LOSERS* MAKING *NOISE!*

OR NO—THAT'S *EXACTLY* WHAT THEY ARE!

I GUESS I'LL *DESTROY* THEM SOMEHOW....

IT'S WHAT I USUALLY DO IN THESE SITUATIONS...

KILL·HELP·PAINT·KICK· ·BEARS·HIPPIES·KOFI ANNA·

POISON BONGO

AND YET MY *ELABORATE* SCHEMES OF *RETRIBUTION* JUST DON'T *SATISFY* ME LIKE THEY *ONCE* DID...

PERHAPS SOMETHING *SIMPLER* IS IN ORDER.

BANG BANG BANG

BUMMER...

BOB THE ANGRY FLOWER in: LYING TO THE LOAN OFFICER

RAAAA!!

HOLY COW! HOW'D THAT HAPPEN?

WHO KNOWS?

I DOUBT IT'LL LAST, THOUGH...

STUMPY'S WORDS PROVE PROPHETIC. BOB IS SOON BACK TO NORMAL AND TRYING TO GET A LOAN...

EVERYTHING APPEARS TO BE IN ORDER HERE, MR. FLOWER. WE JUST HAVE A COUPLE OF ADDITIONAL QUESTIONS FOR TAX PURPOSES...

SHOOT!

HAVE YOU EVER BEEN A GIANT MONSTER?

NO.

NO, OF COURSE NOT. AND YOU HAVE NO HISTORY OF INVOLVEMENT WITH ROBOTS?

SN99 6-4

Bob the Angry Flower

OOOOOO OOOOOOH— CHI-NESE NINJA WAR-RIOR...

WITH YOUR HEART SO COOOLD...

SUB-ZEEE-ROOO!

WHOOOOOOA-YOUR LIFE IS A MYS-TERY...

WHY DO YOU WEAR THAT—

mask?

SUB-ZEE-RO!

IS HE GOING TO SING THAT STUPID SONG EVERY SINGLE TIME I COME OVER?

IS HE EVER...

SUB-ZERO

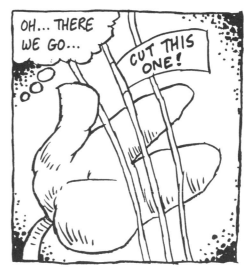

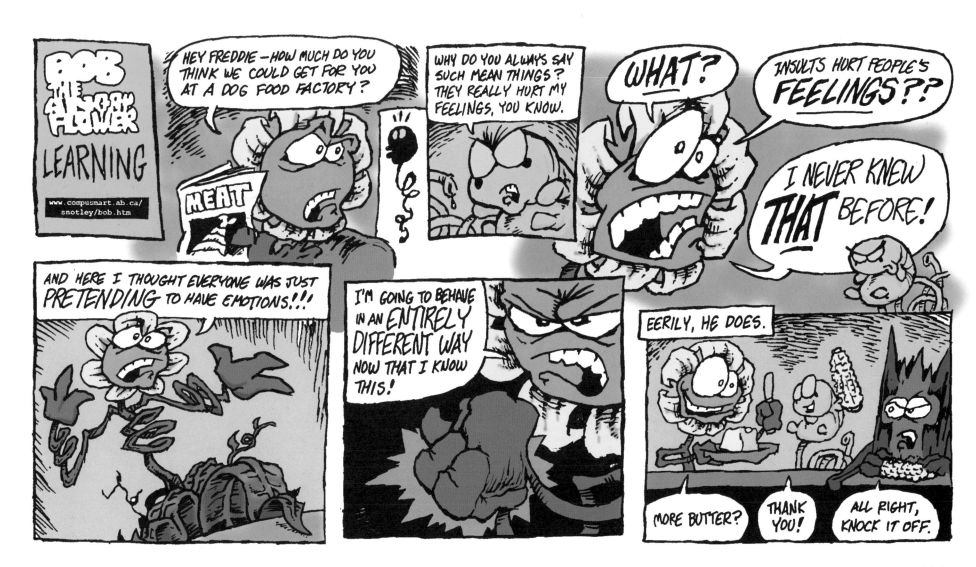

127

128

BOB THE ANGRY FLOWER

"I'VE DECIDED IT'S TIME TO GET A GRIP ON MY TOTAL FIXATION ON *ROBOTS*..."

"HEAR HEAR"

"ABOUT TIME"

":DOES NOT COMPUTE:"

"NOW WE ALL KNOW I DON'T HAVE THE STRENGTH OF WILL TO QUIT ROBOTS *COLD TURKEY*..."

"NOPE."

"NOT EVEN CLOSE."

"INSTEAD, I'LL SHIFT MY OBSESSIONS GRADUALLY AWAY FROM ROBOTS ONTO SIMPLER MACHINES."

"A STEADY STREAM OF *PULLEYS*, *LEVERS* AND *INCLINED PLANES* SHOULD SHAKE THIS THING LOOSE!"

AND IT WOULD'VE WORKED IF NOT FOR **LEVERTRON 13**

"CRUSH!"

"SMASH!"

"LIFT!"

129

131

THE MAN BEHIND THE CURTAIN

HEY KIDS!

WHO LOVES KOOL-AID?

MEEEEE!!!

WE'VE GOT A SPECIAL GUEST TODAY, KIDS!

A GUY WHOSE NAME MEANS "KOOL-AID"!

OH YEAH!

SO LET'S GIVE A GREAT BIG KOOL-AID WELCOME...

...TO KRAFT FOODS C.E.O. ROBERT A. ECKERT!

cough cough

THE KOOL-AID™ PRODUCT LINE HAS LONG BEEN A CORNERSTONE OF OUR BEVERAGE AND DESSERT DIVISION'S PROFITABILITY...

IT WAS A LONG AFTERNOON FOR THE KIDS...

BOB THE ANGRY FLOWER in: WHAT DOES A GIANT SQUIRREL HAVE TO DO WITH angryflower.com?

HI, FOLKS! TODAY I'M GOING TO TALK ABOUT MY WEB SITE!

STUPIDLY, UNTIL NOW IT'S BEEN FOUND AT "http://www.compu smart.ab.ca/snotley/bob.htm."

ERROR

IT WAS DIFFICULT TO TYPE IN, AND IMPOSSIBLE TO REMEMBER!

BUT NOW I'M ESPECIALLY PROUD TO PRESENT—

—OMIGOD! A GIANT SQUIRREL!

WHAT CAN I —OR ANYONE— DO AGAINST SUCH A MONSTER?

IF ONLY IT HAD SOME KIND OF WEAKNESS...

BOB SOON STUMBLES ACROSS AN OBVIOUS ACORN-BASED SOLUTION AND NEUTRALIZES THE SQUIRREL...

UH...WHAT WAS I TALKING ABOUT?

angryflower. com

133

BOB THE ANGRY FLOWER

MAYBE YOU'VE CONVINCED ALL THE NEWSPAPERS THAT YOU'RE **THINKING MACHINES**...

...BUT HERE AT THE BOB THE ANGRY FLOWER ARTIFICIAL INTELLIGENCE INSTITUTE, WE HAVE THE MOST SOPHISTICATED **TURING TEST** QUESTIONS EVER DEVISED!

B.T.A.F.A.I.I.
Test Centre

REST ASSURED, GENTLEMEN — WE WILL DETERMINE WHO TRULY DESERVES TO BE CALLED **INTELLIGENT**!

POWER VAC

EIGHTEEN GRUELING HOURS LATER...

SO HOW ARE THE A.I. TESTS GOING?

INCONCLUSIVE!

THEY **REFUSE** TO ANSWER **ANY** OF MY QUESTIONS!

BUT THEY'RE **CRAZY** IF THEY THINK THEY CAN DEFEAT ME!

I'LL **CRUSH** THEM!

...THAT SHOVEL'S READY TO CRACK, I **KNOW** IT!

BUT THE SHOVEL DOESN'T CRACK, AND OVER THE NEXT FEW DAYS, NEITHER DOES THE BOX, THE CLOCK, OR THE VACUUM CLEANER!

I OBVIOUSLY DIDN'T GIVE THESE THINGS ENOUGH CREDIT! THEY'RE **BRILLIANT**! POSSIBLY EVEN SMARTER THAN **ME**!

I'LL BUY THAT.

135

Random notes

p. 18. This features the reappearance from the first book of capitalist Aung Kung Sui, Bob's most non-repeating nemesis. I still feel he has big plans for Bob, though.

p. 22. This cartoon was conceived and drawn under the influence, if y'know what I mean. It was a total mess, and, I thought, ample evidence of why you shouldn't draw cartoons while stoned. Ho ho ho. How naive I was. This is also one of the few times that Bob ever admits that he's in a cartoon, a conceit used way too much these days.

p. 24. Let's face it -- a lot of problems would go away if we were all just a bit smarter... Note also the sound effect in the fifth panel.

p. 25. Still one of my favorite cartoons, and a true story, except for the invisible cow.

p. 26. For some reason when I was putting cartoons on the Internet I missed this one, so this is a book-only strip. Yee-ha! This is one of the few hot-looking girls I've ever done, and I did it by almost completely copying her from that Mariah Carey album cover. Someday I'll figure out how to draw girls...

p. 27. Bob's eyebrows in the third panel have a particularly sculpted look to them, and that became a standard part of how I drew Bob for the next few months. That's how a character's look evolves: little changes that take hold.

p. 32. That's me sitting in the back of the bus in the first panel.

p. 34. I don't believe in God, in case you were wondering.

p. 35. In the movie *Heavy Metal* there's a scene where some goofy evil warlord bellows Bob's big line there. His armies sweep across the land, slaying not only those who opposed them but pretty much everybody, as far as I could tell. I ask you; was that really necessary?

p. 37. Ah, Kofi, hands down my favorite semi-recurring character. Though he's usually at the receiving end of some humiliation at Bob's hands, I have great sympathy for his uphill efforts to get the inhabitants of Bob's universe to be civilized to each other.

p. 38. This was actually supposed to run the previous Christmas in *See Magazine*, but they FUCKING FORGOT IT, AFTER I BUSTED MY ASS TO GET IT TO THEM IN TIME! So I just used it next year.

p. 41. I love this cartoon. As always, Bob sees the shortcut.

p. 43. I was shocked at how well that seventh panel turned out.

p. 45. Another favorite. And some girls, I've found, don't seem to mind the Lenin banners...

p. 49. My favorite joke in this one is the first panel. And how come I never write punchlines like this any more?

p. 50. It's the tiniest details that stick with you when you draw these things. I never read this cartoon without paying special attention to Freddie's sliced-open innards.

p. 52. Appallingly, that's my father Grant Notley hiding in the corner of the seventh panel. It's appalling because he died in a plane crash when I was 14. But hey, it's all grist for the cartooning mill, right?

p. 53. The first Bob-bot.

p. 61. Expected to get in trouble for the first two names on Bob's list, but nobody noticed.

p. 62. Okay, personal story here, so be warned. I love this cartoon -- it's one of my all time favorites. However, in the last few months of my mother's life, she started to intensely dislike my cartoon, saying that it was "too violent' and such. When I asked her which ones she meant, she didn't really know. She said there was one cartoon about someone with knives sticking out all over her body. Huh? Knives? I had no idea what she was talking about. Only later did I realize she meant this one. I'm pretty sure the real reason she didn't like it was Louise's admittedly icky puckered terminal neck. Oh well. I still like it.

p. 63. Continuing the "headless" theme, here. I'd read somewhere that Winona Ryder's favorite novel was *Catcher in the Rye*, so that gave me an excuse to put her in the cartoon. Also, I'd like to remind everybody that sushi is delicious.

p. 64. This would have been a completely typical strip except that when it came time to draw the third panel, it occurred to me to do what I ended up doing. Now it's one of my favorites, and I've never really been able to pull that kind of layout trickery off as well again.

p. 65. And there's nothing like following up a good cartoon with a lame one.

p. 66. True story, except nobody actually had the guts to go dislodge the fat monster. Plus I think she did have a face.

p. 67. Do I really care about this apostrophe stuff? Let me put it this way: besides being a cartoonist, I'm also a proofreader. Plus, of course, there was the follow-up on p. 130.

p. 69. A rare moment of camaraderie for the boys before everything goes to Hell. Bob's big regret, of course, is really my big regret; I always wanted to see *Dune* on the big screen. There have a been a number of attempts to figure out what Freddie's regret is supposed to mean. I drew it meaning that he regretted getting in the car that afternoon, but a friend pointed out another thing: Freddie can fly, so he's regretting strapping himself to the falling car.

p. 70. Guess what TV show I'd suddenly become obsessed with?

p. 72. Since this cartoon, I've received e-mails from Dungeons and Dragons players who have changed the definition of a Gelatinous Cube to include the fact that it yells "CUBE!" all the time. As it should be.

p. 75. Guess how tall I am.

p. 76. This cartoon launches a seven-strip thematic arc, the theme of which could be loosely articulated as "International Affairs," or more broadly, "People Killing Each Other." Watching the U.S. Hitler-making machine swing into place above Osama Bin Laden left me feeling militarized for months.

p. 77. Bears and robots are my stand-ins for any warring factions. It's a bit tough to keep it fair, since my natural tendencies are to side with the robots, but I try.

p. 80. Ah, Jingles. For the record, the full names of the Fun Brigade are Captain Montgomery Fun, Mrs. Edith Fun, Lieutenant Garth Mirth, and Corporal Arkady Cheer. I think these guys should get a TV show.

p. 82. The second Bob-bot.

p. 84. The tricky bit to this one is that the layout of the first panel mirrors the layout of the whole cartoon. How about that! Plus, note the obvious drug paraphernalia on Bob's drawing table. Purely for show, of course.

p. 85. Another personal favorite. This one received some hate mail, as I was hoping; the buttons of daily newspaper readers are easily pushed. The stinger for most people was the depiction of Christ on the cross, though one guy actually got mad at the burning bush as well. Only one person (the same guy, actually) was correctly offended at the implication that God was shilling for the phone company.

p. 86. Another personal note: my mother died the week I drew this one. You probably wouldn't guess it to read it, and it's kind of a lame cartoon anyway. But it's weird how these cartoons, good or bad, are the guideposts of my life.

p. 87. I love this cartoon, and nobody else did. "Who won the race?" everybody whines. Who cares? All that's important is that whatever happened, Bob doesn't want to think about it. If you must know, it was the sloth. Of course.

p. 88. The third Bob-bot. I recently received an e-mail from somebody requesting an evil robot version of Bob. Come on... *everybody* has an evil robot version. Bob *uses* his robot versions of himself.

p. 89. To me, Bob is that machine and I'm Bob. My favorite bit is Stumpy's three-balloon gasp.

p. 90. It's a constant mystery to me the way that the quality of the art varies so drastically from week to week. I really liked the way the last one turned out, and yet this one felt really crowded and unsleek. I like the jokes, though.

p. 92. I love this cartoon, and this is the one where I finally settled on how to draw Kofi Annan.

p. 93. Second half of a two-part Kofi Annan story. I knew then that he was a winner.

p. 95. The script for this one was largely written by a friend of mine, a columnist named Garnet Fraser. Apparently this is based on a real Tourette's patient who really did fixate on Oginga Odinga. It seemed only natural to bring them together to talk African politics.

p. 99. I must admit, as of this writing November 1999, I'll be a little disappointed if *something* doesn't happen.

p.103. Ah, the eponymous "Coffee With Sinistar." Here's hoping I don't get sued.

p. 104. One of my best robot cartoons ever, I think. They're wily, those robots. At the same time, my robot obsession was starting to show its bald spots with this cartoon, so a friend of mine ("Oginga Odinga" writer Garnet Fraser) challenged me to go two months without doing robots. Easy, though I did sneak some bears in before bringing robots back for the punchline of "The Will."

p. 105. The reason this one is sideways is because it was the front page of an edition of the *Edmonton Journal* What's On section. That's why there are those floating empty boxes... they held the page numbers for where the articles about those gigs could be found in the section.

p. 110. Man, I love that tank. I'd been noticing for a couple of weeks on CNN lots of footage of tanks driving down road and firing at hillsides. Sorta looked like a war as going on in the middle of Europe and nobody was talking about it. By the time the cartoon ran, people were talking about it, and NATO planes were bombing the hell out of Serbia.

p. 112. The eight-week robot fast comes to an understated close.

p. 113. And wouldn't you know it? Bob's dream came true.

p. 115. I'm startled that it's looking like both of them are going to make it through 1999. This was co-drawn by *Space Cat* cartoonist Fish Griwkowsky, who drew Gornar and the "Bob the Angry Flower." The *Journal* declined to run this one, fearing the wrath of all them God-fearin Albertans, ah gess.

p. 116. I had moved to an apartment facing the busiest part of what passes for the Edmonton scene, and visitors invariably asked if it was loud. Usually it didn't bother me. I don't mind the bar noise, or the cars, or the shouting, trash-can-over-knocking people at 2 in the morning. But that bongo player...? Him I hated.

p. 117. This was my aesthetic homage to the new *Star Wars* movie. The fifth panel was my version of the Pod Race: it was big, visually flashy, and totally lame. But I swear I'll make a character out of Big Brother yet.

p. 118. Drawn in Japan. The last panel has one of my favorite Bobs ever.

p. 119. Three, count 'em, *three* separate plotlines in eight little panels.

p. 120. The *Journal* ran this one, and nobody complained. Fancy that. This and "The Miracle of Life" on p. 98 are my parallel comments on my sister's new baby. She didn't like this one so much.

p. 122. I'm afraid I have to admit that all along I've had the lyrics wrong. It's not "Why do you wear that... mask," it's "Warrior with a... mask." But my version is better.

p. 124. Jack Kirby drew the good MODOKs.

p. 127. In the *Journal*, "Fan-tucking-fastic" read as "Fab-tab-ulous."

p. 128. This cartoon is the story of itself.

p. 130. Please photocopy this cartoon and affix it to a wall at your place of work. Let's stamp this thing out.

p. 136. Somebody is actually building these things, and that retinal scanner really is the proposed safety measure. Sign me up!

Semi-accurate index of characters and other stuff